Piano Exam Pieces

ABRSM Grade 7

Selected from the 2013 & 2014 syllabus

Name

Date of exam

CW00346701

Contents

Editor for ABRSM: Richard Jones

First published in 2012 by ABRSM (Publishing) Ltd,
a wholly owned subsidiary of ABRSM, 24 Portland
Place, London W1B 1LU, United Kingdom
© 2012 by The Associated Board of the Royal
Schools of Music

Music origination by Julia Bovee
Cover by Kate Benjamin & Andy Potts
Printed in England by Halstan & Co. Ltd,
Amersham, Bucks.

FSC
www.fsc.org
MIX
Paper from
responsible sources
FSC™ C109619

Allegro

Third movement from Sonata in A flat, H. 31

C. P. E. Bach
(1714–88)

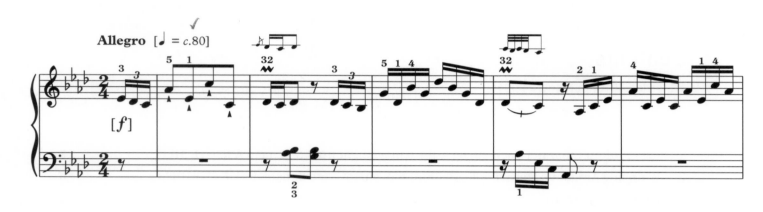

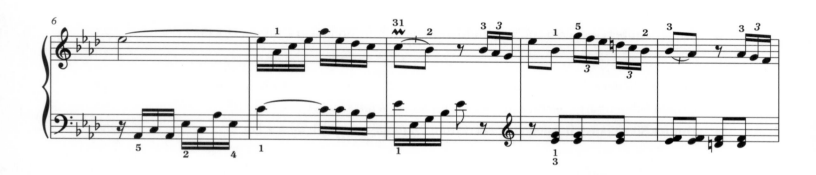

Carl Philipp Emanuel Bach, the second son of the great Johann Sebastian Bach, was taught by his father and became a professional keyboard player, serving for many years as harpsichordist to Frederick the Great in Berlin. He spent the last 20 years of his life as director of music at the five principal churches in Hamburg. C. P. E. Bach is well known as author of one of the most influential treatises of the 18th century, the *Versuch über die wahre Art das Clavier zu spielen* (Essay on the True Art of Playing Keyboard Instruments; Berlin, 1753–62). However, he was also a prolific composer – his works for keyboard alone number over 350. Many of them illustrate the so-called *empfindsamer Stil* (expressive style), which became popular throughout Germany in the mid-18th century.

This Allegro forms the finale of the Sonata in A flat (H. 31), the second of the *Sei sonate per cembalo*, Op. 2. These are known as the Württemberg Sonatas because C. P. E. Bach dedicated them to his pupil Duke Carl Eugen of Württemberg.

Source: *Sei sonate per cembalo*, Op. 2 (Nuremberg: Haffner, 1744)

© 1983 by The Associated Board of the Royal Schools of Music
Adapted from C. P. E. Bach: *Selected Keyboard Works*, Book III, edited by Howard Ferguson (ABRSM)

4

A:2

Allegro

Third movement from Sonata in C, K. 279/189d

W. A. Mozart
(1756–91)

[Musical score: Allegro, ♩ = c.108, 2/4 time, bars 1–24, with handwritten annotations including "operatic character", "pedal notes", "slurs-flute-like agility", and "mp to 116?"]

Mozart's Sonata in C, K. 279, of which this Allegro forms the finale, is the first of a set of six piano sonatas that he wrote at the age of 19 while staying in Munich in early 1775. The set may have been intended for publication, but only one of the six was published during Mozart's lifetime. In 1777 he wrote to his father from Augsburg: 'Here and at Munich I have played all my six sonatas [in public] by heart several times.'

In his performance notes for ABRSM's edition, Denis Matthews wrote that: 'The imprint of Haydn may be detected in the finale of K. 279, and in fact six Haydn sonatas (Hob. XVI/21–6) had been published in 1774' (shortly before Mozart's sonata was composed). He also suggests that accompanying quavers, such as those of bb. 3 and 7–10, should be lightly separated, and that the varied RH slurs of bb. 11–17 call for a 'flute-like agility'.

Source: autograph MS (formerly in Staatsbibliothek zu Berlin, Preussischer Kulturbesitz)

Adapted from Mozart: *Sonatas for Pianoforte*, Vol. I, edited by Stanley Sadie (ABRSM)

Development.

A:3

Sonata in F minor

Kp. 467

Domenico Scarlatti
(1685–1757)

Domenico Scarlatti, Neapolitan by birth, emigrated to Portugal in 1719 and then to Spain in 1728. He spent the rest of his life in Madrid as *maestro de capilla* and music master to the young Princess Maria Barbara, who later became Queen of Spain. Most of his solo keyboard sonatas, well over 500 in number, were composed after his emigration to the Iberian peninsula.

Scarlatti's own description of his sonatas in the preface to the *Essercizi* of 1738, the only collection he published himself, applies equally to the later works, such as this F minor sonata: 'In these compositions, do not expect any profound learning, but rather an ingenious jesting with art.' The second left-hand quaver in b. 41 is *ab* in the source, but might equally be played as *a♮* by analogy to similar patterns in bb. 26 and 100; either note would be acceptable in the exam. Dynamics are left to the player's discretion.

Source: Parma MSS, Vol. XIII, No. 14

Berceuse

B:1

Frank Bridge
(1879–1941)

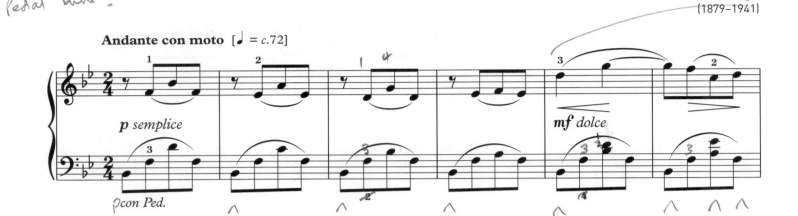

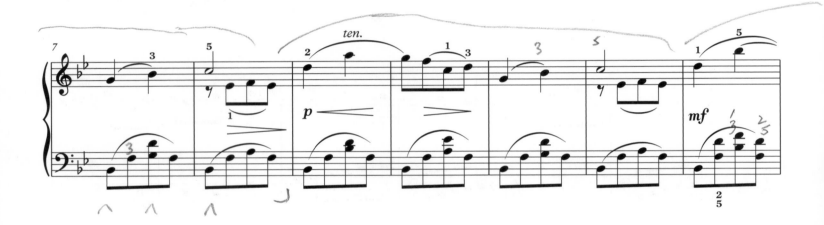

The English composer Frank Bridge studied composition with Charles Stanford at the Royal College of Music. He also played the viola in the Joachim and English Quartets and conducted at the Savoy Theatre and at Covent Garden. His early works are written in a late Romantic style, but subsequently he was strongly influenced by the music of Alban Berg. In the late 1920s he taught the young Benjamin Britten, who then championed his teacher's music. One of Britten's first major successes was *Variations on a Theme of Frank Bridge* (1937).

Bridge's haunting Berceuse of 1901 was written originally for violin and piano. It seems to have become very popular and he made numerous arrangements of it for various combinations of instruments. The solo piano version of 1929 appears to be the last.

Source: *Berceuse* (London: Keith Prowse, 1929)

B:2

Piano Piece in F sharp

S. 193

Franz Liszt
(1811–86)

Franz Liszt was not only a major composer but the most famous and brilliant pianist of his day. Howard Ferguson, editor of *Twenty-one Short Piano Pieces* by Liszt for ABRSM, has written: 'Since most of [his] vast output of piano music, both original and arranged, was obviously intended for the virtuoso, it's easy to forget that he also wrote short and beautiful pieces which are technically undemanding. Moreover, many of these are far more interesting musically than the typically brilliant works.'

This piece in F sharp, S. 193, is undated but is probably a late work, written at a time when Liszt was experimenting with a sort of pre-impressionism and other styles that foreshadow 20th-century music. The texture and the marking *dolcissimo* give the impression of a dreamy nocturne, but a slow tempo is ruled out by the expression mark *appassionato*. In b. 24 the pause applies only to the top note (*eb"*), which should be held after the release of the minim chord. Some of the fingering is Liszt's own, notably that in the RH of bb. 15, 17 and 22.

Source: *F. Liszt, Musicalische Werke*, Series II, Vol. 10 (Leipzig: Breitkopf & Härtel, 1928)

Scherzo and Trio

Third movement from Sonata in A minor, D. 845

B:3

Franz Schubert
(1797–1828)

Scherzo

Allegro vivace [♩. = c.72]

Franz Schubert left 12 complete piano sonatas and, in addition, another 10 that remained unfinished. The Sonata in A minor (D. 845) of 1825, from which this movement is selected, is one of his greatest masterpieces in the genre. It is one of only three sonatas that were published during Schubert's lifetime. When it appeared, a Leipzig critic (in the *Leipziger allgemeine musikalische Zeitung*, 1 March 1826) wrote: 'It moves so freely and originally within its confines, and sometimes so boldly and curiously, that it might not unjustly have been called a fantasia. In that respect it can probably be compared only with the greatest and freest of Beethoven's sonatas.'

The Scherzo, alternately dramatic and lyrical, is full of Schubert's characteristic sudden switches to remote keys. The Trio, in the submediant key, is written in the style of the *Ländler*, an Austrian/South German dance in a slow triple time.

Source: first edition, *Premiere Grande Sonate, Oeuvre 42* (Vienna: A. Pennauer, 1826)

Gr. 5?   octaves - stretching

Trio
Un poco più lento

Scherzo D.C.

Danza de la moza donosa

No. 2 from *Danzas argentinas*, Op. 2

C:1

Alberto Ginastera
(1916–83)

Danza de la moza donosa Dance of the Graceful Young Girl; **Danzas argentinas** Argentinian Dances

The Argentine composer Alberto Ginastera studied at the National Conservatory, Buenos Aires (1936–8), where he later taught. He established his reputation as a composer with two nationalist ballets in the early 1940s. In 1945–7 he visited the USA, where he studied with Aaron Copland. He spent his last years in Geneva. His earlier compositions are written in a nationalist style and make use of Argentinian folk material, but from the late 1950s onwards he cultivated an atonal, expressionist style that involved the use of serialism.

The second of Ginastera's *Danzas argentinas*, Op. 2, of 1937 has a decidedly plaintive tone, but it reaches a climax of great intensity in the parallel dissonant chords of the middle section (bb. 40–52). The penultimate bar is metrically free, so the time signature no longer applies.

© Editions Durand
Reproduced by permission of Universal Music Publishing MGB Ltd. All enquiries about this piece, apart from those directly relating to the exams, should be addressed to Universal Music Publishing MGB Ltd, 20 Fulham Broadway, London SW6 1AH.

C:2

Leicht, zart

No. 1 from *Sechs kleine Klavierstücke*, Op. 19

Arnold Schoenberg
(1874–1951)

Leicht, zart Lightly, delicately; **Sechs kleine Klavierstücke** Six Little Piano Pieces

Arnold Schoenberg was born in Vienna, but became an American citizen in 1941. As composer, teacher and theorist, he ranks as one of the most influential figures in the history of Western music. Around 1900 he was still composing in a post-Wagnerian, late Romantic style, but by 1909 he had abandoned tonality and was writing in a purely atonal idiom.

The *Sechs kleine Klavierstücke*, Op. 19, of 1911, of which the first is selected here, are miniature masterpieces of atonality – not yet organized by the 12-note method, for which Schoenberg is particularly renowned. They are essentially melodic in style, but lack any sense of thematic development.

Allegretto

No. 1 from *Tri fantasticheskikh tantsa*, Op. 5

Edited by Harry Cumpson

Dmitry Shostakovich
(1906–1975)

Tri fantasticheskikh tantsa Three Fantastic Dances

The Russian composer Dmitry Shostakovich learnt the piano as a child from his mother, who was a professional pianist. As a young man he achieved success as a pianist as well as a composer, representing his country at the first International Chopin Piano Competition in Warsaw in 1927. By then he had already composed his earliest piano works, which are written for the instrument with great skill.

The *Three Fantastic Dances*, of which the first is reproduced here, date from 1922 when the composer was only 16 years old. Throughout his career Shostakovich was adept at bizarre fantasy, which is well illustrated in this piece. In b. 6 the first right-hand C might be staccato, as in b. 2.